THE BIG BOOK OF SEARCH & FIND

Tony Tallarico

Kidsbooks®

FIND FREDDIE IN SPACE AND...

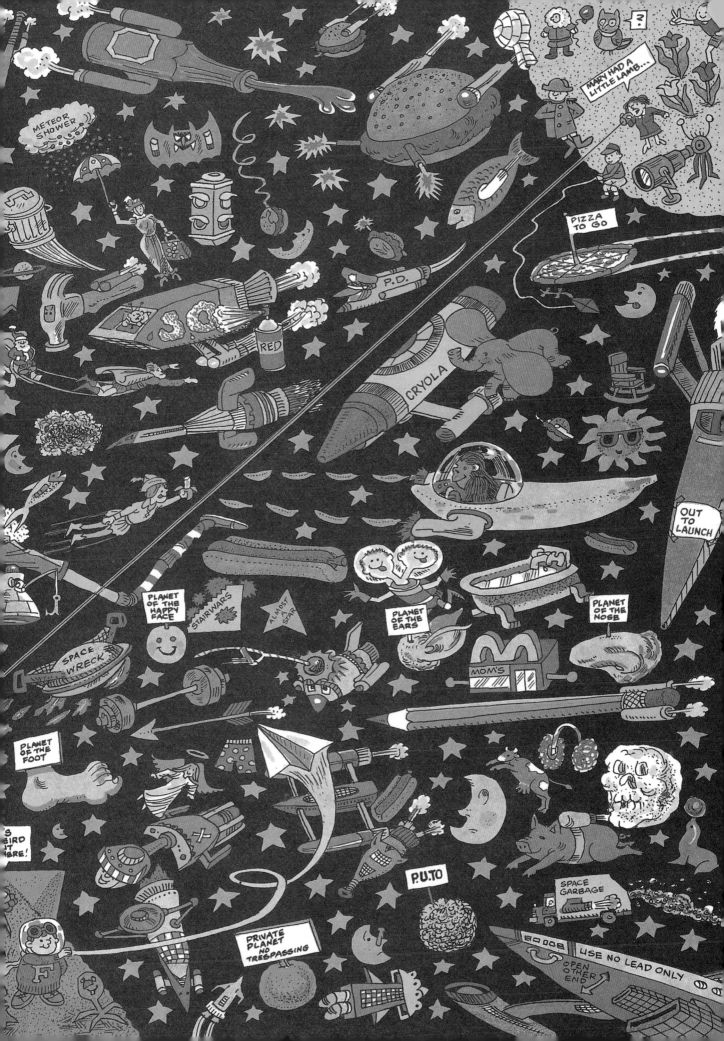

FIND FREDDIE
AT THE
BEACH
AND...

FIND FREDDIE IN MONSTERVILLE AND...

- ❏ Broken heart
- ❏ Carrot
- ❏ Cowboy hat
- ❏ Flowers (2)
- ❏ "For Rent"
- ❏ Gorilla
- ❏ Hose
- ❏ Key
- ❏ Mouse hole
- ❏ Ms. Transylvania
- ❏ Mummy
- ❏ Number 13 (3)
- ❏ Octopus
- ❏ One-eyed monster
- ❏ Owl
- ❏ Parachute
- ❏ Pig
- ❏ Pile of bones
- ❏ Pink hand
- ❏ Pyramid
- ❏ Rat
- ❏ Scary trees (2)
- ❏ Skeleton
- ❏ Skulls (8)
- ❏ Stethoscope
- ❏ Three-legged ghost
- ❏ Tin can
- ❏ Tin man
- ❏ Trick-or-Treat bags (4)
- ❏ Weather vane

FIND FREDDIE
AT THE
AIRPORT
AND...

- ❏ Binoculars
- ❏ Birdcage
- ❏ Chair
- ❏ Clothespins (6)
- ❏ Football
- ❏ Golf club
- ❏ Green checkered pants
- ❏ Guardhouse
- ❏ Hammock
- ❏ Harpoon
- ❏ Hearts (2)
- ❏ Helicopters (2)
- ❏ Hot-air balloon
- ❏ Hot dogs (2)
- ❏ Ice-cream cones (2)
- ❏ Kite
- ❏ Laundry line
- ❏ Locomotive
- ❏ Lost wallet
- ❏ Manhole
- ❏ Paint rollers (2)
- ❏ Parachute
- ❏ Pear
- ❏ "Pequod"
- ❏ Pizza
- ❏ Roller coaster
- ❏ Skier
- ❏ Stretch limo
- ❏ Submarine
- ❏ Toaster
- ❏ Wooden leg

FIND FREDDIE
AT THE
MUSEUM
AND...

- ❏ Airplane
- ❏ Alien
- ❏ Balloons (7)
- ❏ Bather
- ❏ Birdcage
- ❏ Birthday cake
- ❏ Doctor
- ❏ Doghouse
- ❏ Firefighter
- ❏ Fire hydrant
- ❏ "First Prize"
- ❏ Fishing pole
- ❏ Flying carpet
- ❏ Football player
- ❏ Guitar
- ❏ Headless man
- ❏ Hot-air balloon
- ❏ Ice-cream cone
- ❏ Jack-in-the-box
- ❏ Kite
- ❏ Knights (2)
- ❏ Long beard
- ❏ Magnifying glass
- ❏ Princess
- ❏ Quicksand
- ❏ Robin Hood
- ❏ Scuba diver
- ❏ Superman
- ❏ TV antenna
- ❏ Viking ship
- ❏ Watering can
- ❏ Whistle

FIND FREDDIE
IN THE
OLD WEST TOWN
AND...

- ☐ Angel
- ☐ Apple
- ☐ Artist
- ☐ Baby turtle
- ☐ Camel
- ☐ Car
- ☐ Fire hydrant
- ☐ Fishing pole
- ☐ Flowerpot
- ☐ Football
- ☐ Guitar
- ☐ "ICU2"
- ☐ Monster hand
- ☐ Mouse holes (2)
- ☐ Outhouse
- ☐ Pencil
- ☐ Periscope
- ☐ Piano
- ☐ Pink elephant
- ☐ Rabbits (3)
- ☐ Sailboat
- ☐ Saw
- ☐ Smoke signal
- ☐ Soccer ball
- ☐ Stop sign
- ☐ Sun
- ☐ Toasters (5)
- ☐ UFO
- ☐ Umbrellas (2)
- ☐ Upside-down sign
- ☐ "Wet Paint"

FIND FREDDIE AT SCHOOL AND...

- ❏ Air pump
- ❏ Barbells (2)
- ❏ Baseballs (2)
- ❏ Basketballs (3)
- ❏ Bench
- ❏ Briefcases (2)
- ❏ Broken windows (2)
- ❏ Butterfly net
- ❏ Cake
- ❏ Fish (2)
- ❏ Fishing pole
- ❏ Horse
- ❏ Jump rope
- ❏ Magic carpet
- ❏ Mail carrier
- ❏ Mouse
- ❏ Mud puddle
- ❏ Musical notes (3)
- ❏ Paper airplanes (5)
- ❏ Pillow
- ❏ Pumpkin
- ❏ Rabbits (2)
- ❏ Skull
- ❏ Soccer ball
- ❏ Surfboard
- ❏ Swing set
- ❏ Telescope
- ❏ Trash can
- ❏ Tug-of-war
- ❏ Upside-down bucket
- ❏ Window washer

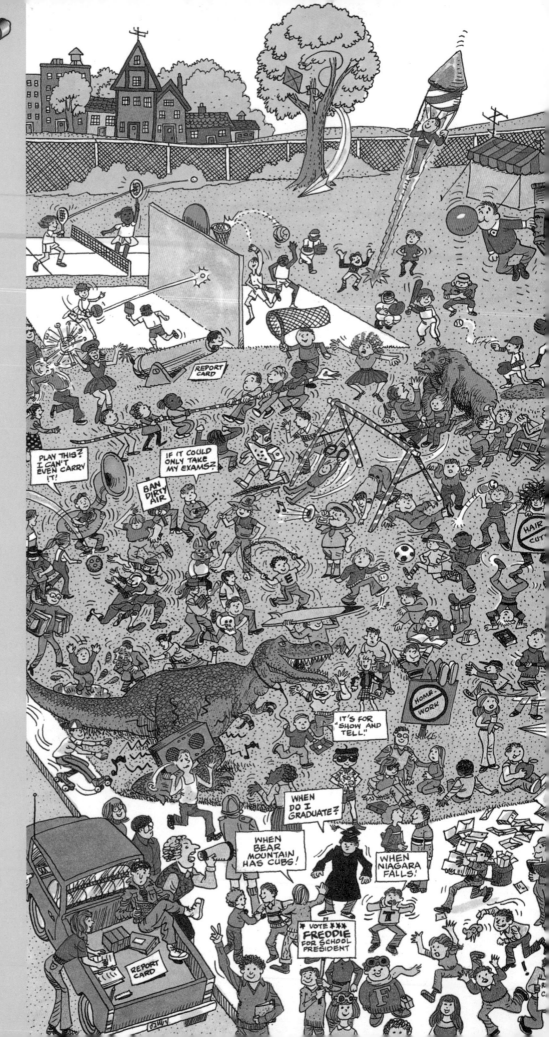

FIND FREDDIE

AT

HOME

AND...

FIND FREDDIE
AT THE
BALLPARK
AND...

- ❏ Balloons (7)
- ❏ Banana
- ❏ Baseball bats (10)
- ❏ Basketball hoop
- ❏ Bicycle
- ❏ Binoculars
- ❏ Blimp
- ❏ Carrot
- ❏ Clipboard
- ❏ Cook
- ❏ Cowboy hat
- ❏ Crown
- ❏ "Detour"
- ❏ Dogs (2)
- ❏ Gorilla
- ❏ Kite
- ❏ Ladder
- ❏ Lawn mower
- ❏ Money
- ❏ Mouse hole
- ❏ Parachutist
- ❏ Periscope
- ❏ Policemen (2)
- ❏ Ripped pants
- ❏ Sombrero
- ❏ Sunbather
- ❏ Sword
- ❏ Tic-tac-toe
- ❏ Toolbox
- ❏ Trash can
- ❏ Turtle
- ❏ Upside-down fan

FIND FREDDIE
AMONG THESE
FRIENDLY
FOREIGNERS
AND...

- ❏ Anchor
- ❏ Antlers
- ❏ Baby
- ❏ Balloon
- ❏ Barn
- ❏ Bullfighter
- ❏ Camera
- ❏ Cheese
- ❏ Clothespins (4)
- ❏ Deer (2)
- ❏ Eagle scout
- ❏ Eiffel Tower
- ❏ Elephant
- ❏ Fisherman
- ❏ Greek ruins
- ❏ Kite
- ❏ Oil well
- ❏ Owl
- ❏ Panda
- ❏ Picnic basket
- ❏ Piggy bank
- ❏ Pyramid
- ❏ Rain slicker
- ❏ Telescope
- ❏ Umbrellas (2)
- ❏ Viking
- ❏ Windmill

FIND FREDDIE
IN THIS
BLISTERY BLIZZARD
AND...

- ❏ Airplane
- ❏ Aliens (2)
- ❏ Baseball
- ❏ Box
- ❏ Campfire
- ❏ Circus tents (2)
- ❏ Easel
- ❏ Football
- ❏ Heart
- ❏ Helicopter
- ❏ Ice castle
- ❏ Ice skates (6)
- ❏ Jack-o'-lantern
- ❏ Kangaroo
- ❏ Kite
- ❏ Magic carpet
- ❏ Paintbrush
- ❏ Periscope
- ❏ Santa Claus
- ❏ Skis (4)
- ❏ Sleds (5)
- ❏ Spaceship
- ❏ Stars (2)
- ❏ Tennis racket
- ❏ Tin man
- ❏ Tombstone
- ❏ Top hats (2)

SEARCH FOR SUSIE
IN THE
GAME ROOM
AND...

- ❑ Banana
- ❑ Blindfold
- ❑ Bucket
- ❑ Cat
- ❑ Catcher's mitt
- ❑ Donkeys (2)
- ❑ "Don't Be Quiet"
- ❑ Dustpan
- ❑ Fake nose
- ❑ Flying reptile
- ❑ Football
- ❑ Graduate's hat
- ❑ Green bug
- ❑ Guitar
- ❑ Hairbrush
- ❑ Juggler
- ❑ Kangaroo
- ❑ Mouse house
- ❑ Picture frame
- ❑ Pie
- ❑ Rabbits (3)
- ❑ Ring toss
- ❑ Roller skate
- ❑ Sailboat
- ❑ Scarf
- ❑ Snake
- ❑ Toolbox
- ❑ Umbrella
- ❑ Watering can
- ❑ Watermelon slice
- ❑ Worm

SEARCH FOR SUSIE
IN THE
BIG FUN PARK
AND...

- ☐ Baby dinosaurs (2)
- ☐ Bench
- ☐ Billy goat
- ☐ Blue jay
- ☐ Boot
- ☐ Cactus
- ☐ Cat
- ☐ Coffeepot
- ☐ Dollar sign
- ☐ Elephants (3)
- ☐ Fire hydrant
- ☐ Giraffes (2)
- ☐ Hamburgers (3)
- ☐ Kite
- ☐ Mice (2)
- ☐ Monkey
- ☐ Necklace
- ☐ Owl
- ☐ Pelican
- ☐ Penguin
- ☐ Periscopes (2)
- ☐ Pigs (4)
- ☐ Sailboat
- ☐ Sailor hat
- ☐ Scarecrow
- ☐ Stars (6)
- ☐ Wagon
- ☐ Susie's mom
- ☐ Telescope
- ☐ Unicorn
- ☐ Warthog
- ☐ Wolf

SEARCH FOR SUSIE
AT THE
WATER RIDE
AND...

- ❏ Apple
- ❏ Beach ball
- ❏ Bib
- ❏ Bull
- ❏ Candles (2)
- ❏ Cats (2)
- ❏ Earring
- ❏ Elephants (2)
- ❏ Fishing pole
- ❏ Gorilla
- ❏ Hearts (2)
- ❏ Hot dog
- ❏ Kangaroo
- ❏ Paper bag
- ❏ Parrot
- ❏ Pencil
- ❏ Periscope
- ❏ Picnic basket
- ❏ Pitcher
- ❏ Puddles (4)
- ❏ Rabbits (2)
- ❏ Scuba diver
- ❏ Sheep
- ❏ Snakes (2)
- ❏ Sunglasses (2)
- ❏ Tents (3)
- ❏ Tire
- ❏ Turtle
- ❏ Wooden leg

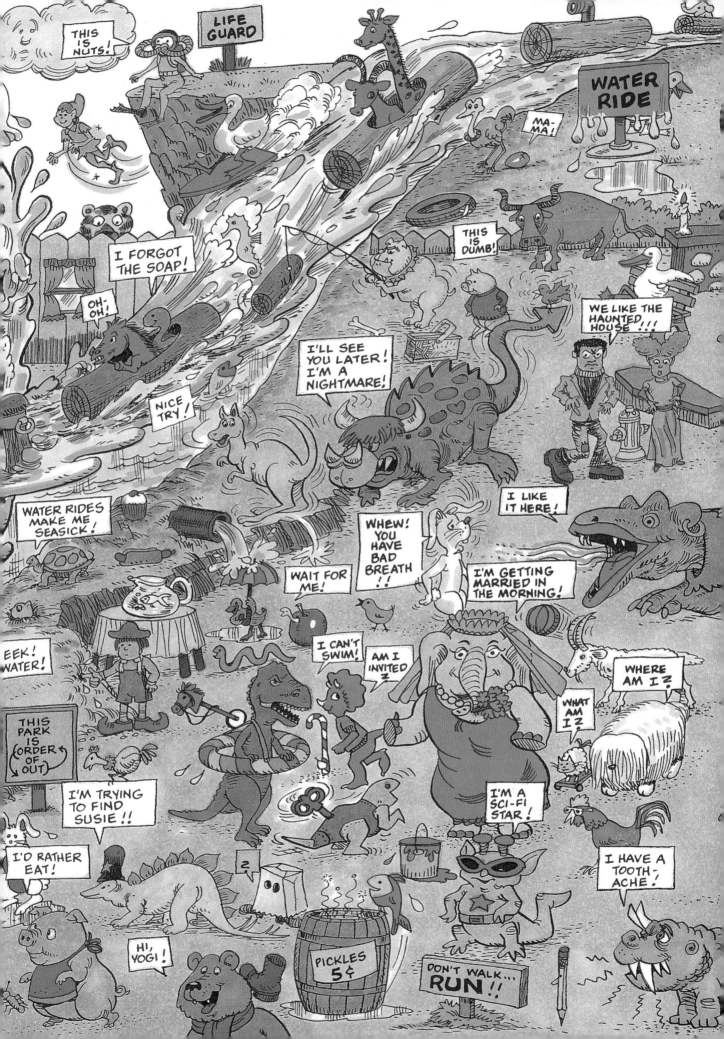

SEARCH FOR SUSIE

AT THE
FUN HOUSE
AND...

- ❏ Airplane
- ❏ Alligator
- ❏ Anchor
- ❏ Banana peel
- ❏ Baseball cap
- ❏ Bowling ball
- ❏ Cactus
- ❏ Candle
- ❏ Chef's hat
- ❏ Clothespin
- ❏ Comb
- ❏ Curtains
- ❏ Diving board
- ❏ Flowers (2)
- ❏ Football
- ❏ Giraffes (2)
- ❏ Lamp
- ❏ Lollipop
- ❏ Lost boots (2)
- ❏ Masks (2)
- ❏ Mice (2)
- ❏ Pinocchio
- ❏ Pot
- ❏ Rabbits (3)
- ❏ Sailor hat
- ❏ Television
- ❏ Turtles (2)
- ❏ Vase
- ❏ Wall clocks (2)
- ❏ Wristwatch

SEARCH FOR SUSIE
ON THE
ROCK AND ROLLER COASTER
AND...

- ☐ Barbell
- ☐ Beach ball
- ☐ Bowling ball
- ☐ Buffalo
- ☐ Cactus
- ☐ Candy cane
- ☐ Doghouse
- ☐ Dogs (2)
- ☐ Eight ball
- ☐ Elephants (2)
- ☐ Fishercat
- ☐ Football
- ☐ Giraffes (3)
- ☐ Hockey stick
- ☐ Hot dog
- ☐ Ice-cream cone
- ☐ Mailbox
- ☐ Mice (3)
- ☐ Pencil
- ☐ Periscope
- ☐ Pigs (2)
- ☐ Pot
- ☐ Snake
- ☐ Swings
- ☐ Target
- ☐ Telescope
- ☐ Tin can
- ☐ Train engine
- ☐ Turtles (2)
- ☐ Well

SEARCH FOR SUSIE
ON THE
BUMPER CARS
AND...

- ☐ Alligator
- ☐ Automobile
- ☐ Banana peel
- ☐ Baseball cap
- ☐ Birds (3)
- ☐ Bow ties (2)
- ☐ Easel
- ☐ Elephants (2)
- ☐ Football player
- ☐ Lions (2)
- ☐ Manhole
- ☐ Necklace
- ☐ Old shoe
- ☐ Paintbrush
- ☐ "Pay Toll Here"
- ☐ Propeller
- ☐ Rope
- ☐ Sailboat
- ☐ Scarves (2)
- ☐ Seal
- ☐ Snake
- ☐ Sneaker car
- ☐ Straw
- ☐ Surfboard
- ☐ Table
- ☐ Tiger
- ☐ Top hat
- ☐ Tuba
- ☐ Turtle

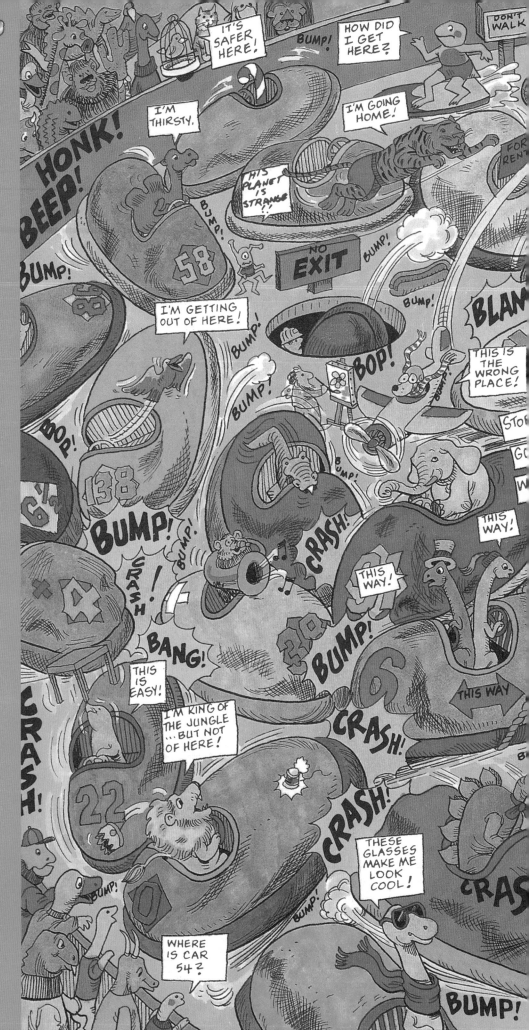

SEARCH FOR SUSIE
ON THE
GIANT SWINGS
AND...

- ❏ Arrow
- ❏ Bears (2)
- ❏ Birdcage
- ❏ Bowling ball
- ❏ Candle
- ❏ Cat
- ❏ Dart
- ❏ Dogs (3)
- ❏ Elephants (2)
- ❏ Fishhook
- ❏ Football helmet
- ❏ Hot dog
- ❏ Ice skate
- ❏ Lamps (2)
- ❏ Lollipop
- ❏ Lost sneaker
- ❏ Magic lamp
- ❏ Monkey
- ❏ Mouse
- ❏ Penguin
- ❏ Propeller hat
- ❏ Rocket
- ❏ Scissors
- ❏ Soccer ball
- ❏ Sock
- ❏ Superhero
- ❏ Yo-yo

LOOK FOR LAURA
ON
PLANET MAXXX
AND...

- ❏ Asteroid for rent
- ❏ Banana
- ❏ Baseball
- ❏ Birds (2)
- ❏ Briefcase
- ❏ Broom
- ❏ Clocks (4)
- ❏ Duck
- ❏ Footballs (2)
- ❏ Fork
- ❏ Hammer
- ❏ Helmet
- ❏ Horse
- ❏ Hot dog
- ❏ Monkey
- ❏ Moon
- ❏ Mushroom
- ❏ Paper airplane
- ❏ Plumber's plunger
- ❏ Pyramid
- ❏ Robot
- ❏ Skateboard
- ❏ Snake
- ❏ Star
- ❏ Sunglasses
- ❏ Tire
- ❏ Tree

LOOK FOR LAURA
ON A
SKI SLOPE
IN THE ALPS
AND...

- ❏ Balloon
- ❏ Barrels (2)
- ❏ Car
- ❏ Duck
- ❏ Earmuffs (3 pairs)
- ❏ Easel
- ❏ Elephant
- ❏ Frankenstein's monster
- ❏ Glove
- ❏ Headbands (2)
- ❏ Lamppost
- ❏ Lost boots (2)
- ❏ Lost ski
- ❏ Red bows (3)
- ❏ Scarves (7)
- ❏ Scuba diver
- ❏ Shovel
- ❏ "Soft Snow"
- ❏ Sunbather
- ❏ Telephone
- ❏ Telescope
- ❏ Tent
- ❏ Thrown snowball
- ❏ Train
- ❏ Tree

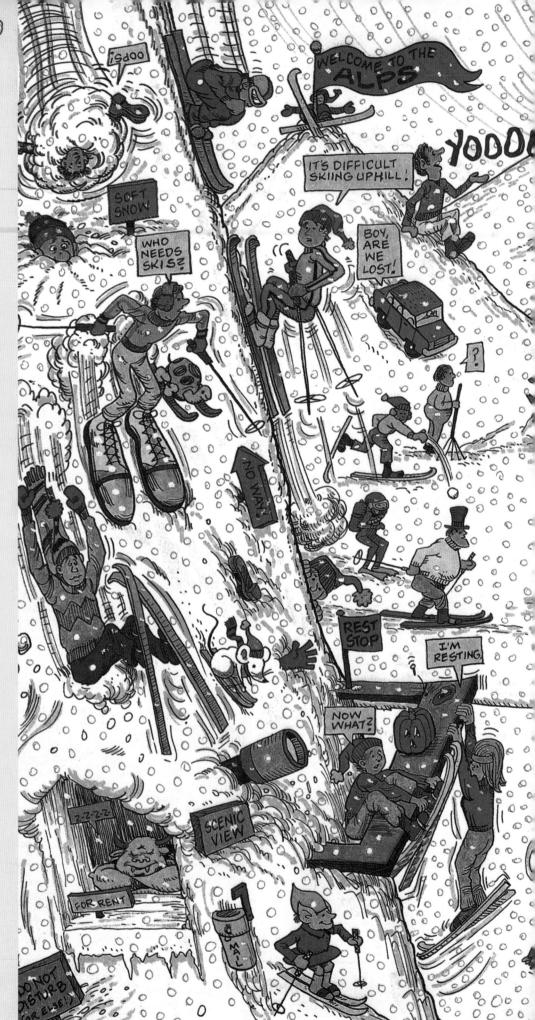

LOOK FOR LAURA
AT
SUMMER CAMP
AND...

- ❏ Arrow
- ❏ Baseball
- ❏ Bone
- ❏ Bottle
- ❏ Bucket
- ❏ Campfire
- ❏ Car
- ❏ Dog
- ❏ Flowers (5)
- ❏ Flying bat
- ❏ Football
- ❏ Ghost
- ❏ Giraffe
- ❏ Graduate's hat
- ❏ Hammock
- ❏ Hose
- ❏ Jester's hat
- ❏ Kite
- ❏ Old tire
- ❏ Painted egg
- ❏ "Poison Ivy"
- ❏ Reindeer
- ❏ Rowboat
- ❏ Sailboat
- ❏ Snakes (3)
- ❏ Spray can
- ❏ Tattoo
- ❏ Tic-tac-toe
- ❏ Toy train
- ❏ Trash can
- ❏ Treasure chest
- ❏ Truck
- ❏ Turtle
- ❏ Wooden spoon

LOOK FOR LAURA
AT THE
WELCOME HOME PARTY
AND...

- ❏ Balloons (2)
- ❏ Baseball
- ❏ Boot
- ❏ Bouquet of flowers
- ❏ Bowling ball
- ❏ Broom
- ❏ Dog
- ❏ Donut
- ❏ Fish
- ❏ Flowerpot
- ❏ Half-moons (2)
- ❏ Hearts (2)
- ❏ Ice-cream cone
- ❏ Manhole
- ❏ Nose
- ❏ Old tire
- ❏ Paddle
- ❏ Pail
- ❏ Pocket watch
- ❏ Scissors
- ❏ Screwdriver
- ❏ Stars (8)
- ❏ Straw
- ❏ Sunglasses
- ❏ Swiss cheese
- ❏ Top hat
- ❏ Turtle
- ❏ Yo-yo

LOOK FOR LAURA

AT THE

WATERING HOLE

AND...

- ☐ Baby bird
- ☐ Birdcage
- ☐ Briefcase
- ☐ Clothespins (2)
- ☐ Coconuts (4)
- ☐ Donkey
- ☐ Duck
- ☐ Feather
- ☐ Fish (3)
- ☐ Giraffe
- ☐ Headband
- ☐ Heart
- ☐ Hippo
- ☐ Leopard
- ☐ Lions (2)
- ☐ Log
- ☐ Lollipop
- ☐ Octopus
- ☐ Ping-Pong paddle
- ☐ Radio
- ☐ Rhinoceros
- ☐ Robot
- ☐ Snake
- ☐ Turtle
- ☐ TV set
- ☐ Worm

LOOK FOR LAURA
IN
EUROPE
AND...

- ☐ Backpacks (2)
- ☐ Basket
- ☐ Bear
- ☐ "Black Sea"
- ☐ Book
- ☐ Bus
- ☐ Cars (2)
- ☐ Castle
- ☐ Cowboy hat
- ☐ Crown
- ☐ Dog
- ☐ Eyeglasses
- ☐ Fishing pole
- ☐ Ghost
- ☐ Greek ruin
- ☐ Head scarf
- ☐ Hot-air balloon
- ☐ Knight
- ☐ Maps (2)
- ☐ Moose
- ☐ Mountain climber
- ☐ Sailboat
- ☐ Scarves (2)
- ☐ Sleigh
- ☐ Suitcase
- ☐ Tunnel
- ☐ Windmill
- ☐ Yellow bird

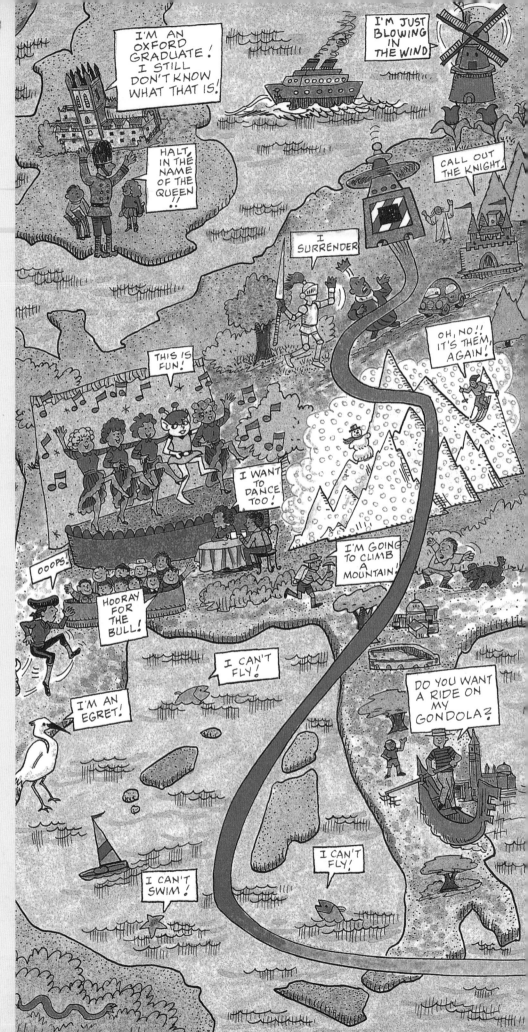

LOOK
FOR LAURA
AT THE
CIRCUS
AND...

- Bandanas (2)
- Bicycle
- Bird
- Broom
- Car
- Cat
- Crown
- Drum
- Earmuff
- Flowerpot
- Flying shoe
- Football helmet
- Giraffe
- Lamp
- Mustaches (4)
- Padlock
- Paper bag
- Periscope
- Pointed hats (3)
- Propellers (2)
- Rabbit
- Ring of fire
- Sailor
- Santa Claus
- Straw hat
- Unhappy face
- Unicorn
- Whip

LOOK FOR LAURA
AT
SCHOOL
AND...

- ☐ Basketball
- ☐ Birdhouse
- ☐ Bookend
- ☐ Boot
- ☐ Clock
- ☐ Cupcake
- ☐ Dog
- ☐ Drum set
- ☐ Earmuffs
- ☐ Eyeglasses (3)
- ☐ Fork
- ☐ Globe
- ☐ Golf club
- ☐ Hair bows (5)
- ☐ Joke book
- ☐ Jump rope
- ☐ Mitten
- ☐ Pen
- ☐ Pencils (4)
- ☐ Rabbit
- ☐ Scarf
- ☐ Soccer ball
- ☐ Sock
- ☐ Straw hat
- ☐ Teddy bear
- ☐ Three-legged stool
- ☐ Tic-tac-toe
- ☐ Top hat
- ☐ TV set

SEARCH FOR SAM
AT THE
FAT CAT GYM
AND...

- ❏ Book
- ❏ Bowling ball
- ❏ Breaking rope
- ❏ Burned feet
- ❏ Cat food dish
- ❏ Catnap
- ❏ Clipboard
- ❏ Cool cat
- ❏ Dog bone
- ❏ "Do Not Touch"
- ❏ Escaped bird
- ❏ Fish (2)
- ❏ Fishbowl
- ❏ Fish skeletons (6)
- ❏ Hearts (3)
- ❏ Helmet
- ❏ Ice-cream cones (2)
- ❏ Jump rope
- ❏ Money
- ❏ Pair of boxing gloves
- ❏ Pizza
- ❏ Prisoner
- ❏ Punching bags (2)
- ❏ Rats (3)
- ❏ Stationary bike
- ❏ Sweat bands (13)
- ❏ Tail warmer
- ❏ Torn pants
- ❏ Window
- ❏ Yoga mats (3)

SEARCH FOR SAM
IN
CAT CITY
AND...

SEARCH FOR SAM
AT THE
MIDNIGHT MEOWING
AND...

- ❏ Baseball
- ❏ Baseball bat
- ❏ Birdhouse
- ❏ Can
- ❏ Cannon
- ❏ Cloud
- ❏ Egg
- ❏ Fishbowl
- ❏ Fish skeletons (2)
- ❏ Football
- ❏ Gate
- ❏ Jack-o'-lantern
- ❏ Light
- ❏ Microphone
- ❏ Moon
- ❏ "No Welcome" mat
- ❏ Old tire
- ❏ Piggy bank
- ❏ Police car
- ❏ Policeman
- ❏ Pot
- ❏ Record player
- ❏ Rolling pin
- ❏ Spoon
- ❏ Stacks of paper (2)
- ❏ Stars (4)
- ❏ Table
- ❏ Tent
- ❏ UFO
- ❏ Wood planks (3)
- ❏ Yo-yo

SEARCH
FOR SAM
AT THE
DISCO
AND...

- ☐ Ballerina
- ☐ Blue rhinos (2)
- ☐ Breakdance cat
- ☐ Cat blowing horn
- ☐ Chef
- ☐ Clipboard
- ☐ Clown cat
- ☐ Cowboy cat
- ☐ Disco ball
- ☐ Doctor
- ☐ Dog
- ☐ Duck
- ☐ Earplug seller
- ☐ Earrings
- ☐ Eye patch
- ☐ Flowerpot
- ☐ Hard hat
- ☐ Karate cat
- ☐ Lampshade
- ☐ Pig
- ☐ Pirate sword
- ☐ Pizza
- ☐ Police officer
- ☐ Record player
- ☐ Roller skates
- ☐ Skis
- ☐ Snow cat
- ☐ Speakers (10)
- ☐ Sunglasses
- ☐ Swinging cat
- ☐ Top hat
- ☐ Wooden leg

SEARCH FOR SAM IN ANCIENT EGYPT AND...

- ❏ Antenna
- ❏ Arrows (4)
- ❏ Boats (2)
- ❏ Boxes (3)
- ❏ Bucket
- ❏ Cats in bikinis (2)
- ❏ Falling coconuts (2)
- ❏ Fan
- ❏ Fire
- ❏ Fishing poles (2)
- ❏ Flying carpet
- ❏ Guard cats (5)
- ❏ Hippo
- ❏ Horse
- ❏ Jester
- ❏ Mummies (2)
- ❏ Palm trees (2)
- ❏ Pyramids (8)
- ❏ Quicksand
- ❏ Red birds (4)
- ❏ Red bow
- ❏ Rolled paper
- ❏ Sand pail
- ❏ Shovel
- ❏ Smiley face
- ❏ Snakes (2)
- ❏ Snowman
- ❏ Taxi
- ❏ Telephone
- ❏ Umbrella

SEARCH FOR SAM WITH THE DOGBUSTERS AND...

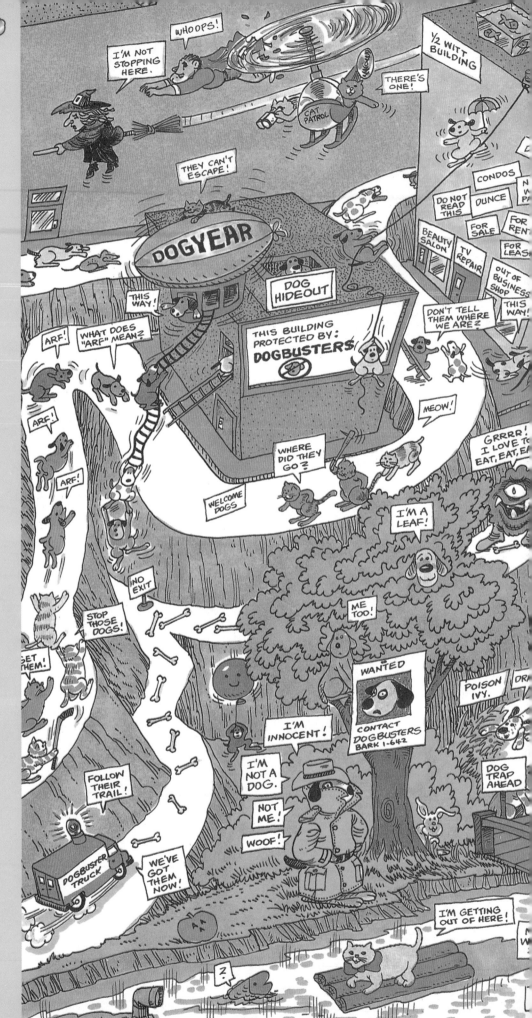

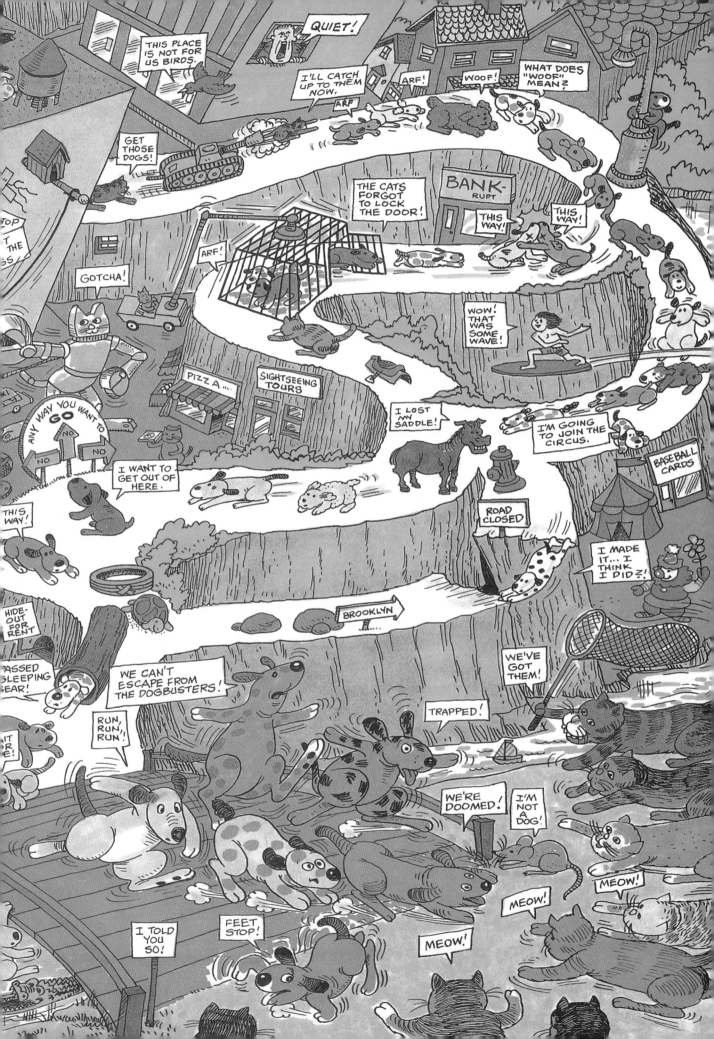

SEARCH FOR SAM
AT THE
NORTH POLE
AND...

- ❏ Badge
- ❏ Bells (2)
- ❏ Bread
- ❏ Broken chair
- ❏ Cactus
- ❏ Campfire
- ❏ Chef's hat
- ❏ Clock
- ❏ Fish
- ❏ Fishing pole
- ❏ Football
- ❏ Globe
- ❏ Green sock
- ❏ Hammer
- ❏ Kite
- ❏ Locomotive
- ❏ Miner's hat
- ❏ Musical notes (3)
- ❏ Ornament
- ❏ Pizza
- ❏ Polar bear
- ❏ Reindeer
- ❏ Satellite dish
- ❏ Singing birds (2)
- ❏ Skier
- ❏ Snake with a hat
- ❏ Stepladder
- ❏ Toy car
- ❏ Yo-yo
- ❏ Zebras (2)

FIND FRANKIE
AT THE
MONSTER CLUB MEETING
AND...

- ❏ Bow ties (3)
- ❏ Cane
- ❏ Cracked mirror
- ❏ Eyeglasses
- ❏ Jack-o'-lantern
- ❏ Knight in armor
- ❏ Mouse holes (2)
- ❏ Mummy
- ❏ Neckties (4)
- ❏ Parrot
- ❏ Pirate
- ❏ Propeller
- ❏ Rain boots
- ❏ Scar
- ❏ Shelves (2)
- ❏ Ski hat
- ❏ Smelly monster
- ❏ Snake
- ❏ Straw
- ❏ Suspenders
- ❏ Television
- ❏ Towel
- ❏ Turtle
- ❏ Witch
- ❏ Wooden club
- ❏ Yo-yo

FIND FRANKIE
IN THE
SUPERMARKET
AND...

FIND FRANKIE
AT THE
YUM-YUM
EMPORIUM
AND...

- Alien
- Baseball cap
- Bib
- Birdcage
- Book
- Booster seat
- Briefcase
- Crown
- Crutch
- Cupcake
- Duck
- Eye patch
- Food fight
- Football player
- Ice-cream cone
- Mailbox
- Man with fingers in ears
- Napkin dispensers (2)
- Pearl necklaces (2)
- Pig
- Pizza
- Rain slicker
- Red bandanas (2)
- Red hats (2)
- Salt shaker
- Shark fin
- Straws (2)
- Sunglasses (2)
- Suspenders
- Volcano

FIND FRANKIE
AT THE
AQUARIUM
AND...

FIND FRANKIE
AT THE
ARCADE
AND...

- ☐ Balloon
- ☐ Baseball
- ☐ Beach ball
- ☐ Bees (2)
- ☐ Birdcage
- ☐ Black cat
- ☐ Book
- ☐ Bucket
- ☐ Cannon
- ☐ Dracula
- ☐ Faucet
- ☐ Football
- ☐ Hard hat
- ☐ Jack-o'-lantern
- ☐ Lightning
- ☐ Maze
- ☐ Mouse
- ☐ Mummy
- ☐ Policeman
- ☐ Rocket
- ☐ Sailor hat
- ☐ Stuffed animal
- ☐ Sunglasses
- ☐ Target
- ☐ Top hat
- ☐ Turtle
- ☐ Umbrella
- ☐ Yo-yo

FIND FRANKIE
AT THE
ROWDY ROLLER RINK
AND...

FIND FRANKIE
AT THE
MONSTERS'
NEW
CLUBHOUSE
AND...

- ❏ Bee
- ❏ Broom
- ❏ Candles (2)
- ❏ Clouds (2)
- ❏ Cobweb
- ❏ Doormat
- ❏ Flower
- ❏ Football
- ❏ Heart
- ❏ Light bulb
- ❏ Mouse hole
- ❏ Mustache
- ❏ Neckties (2)
- ❏ Octopus
- ❏ Pirate
- ❏ Pointed hats (2)
- ❏ Sled
- ❏ Smiling ghosts (2)
- ❏ Smiling star
- ❏ Snake
- ❏ Thirteens (4)
- ❏ Tic-tac-toe
- ❏ Tiny monster
- ❏ Trapdoor
- ❏ Trees (2)
- ❏ Turtle
- ❏ Umbrella
- ❏ Unhappy moon

FIND FRANKIE
AT THE
ZOO
AND...

- ❏ Alligator
- ❏ Artist
- ❏ Blue hats (3)
- ❏ Bucket
- ❏ Carrots (2)
- ❏ Clothesline
- ❏ Fishing pole
- ❏ Half-moon
- ❏ Jack-o'-lantern
- ❏ Kids on fathers' shoulders (2)
- ❏ Knee pads
- ❏ Ladder
- ❏ Matador
- ❏ Orange birds (2)
- ❏ Park bench
- ❏ Periscope
- ❏ Pink flamingo
- ❏ Purple hats (3)
- ❏ Purple sock
- ❏ Rabbits (2)
- ❏ Red bandanas (2)
- ❏ Red hats (4)
- ❏ Stool
- ❏ Strollers (2)
- ❏ Tiger
- ❏ Umbrella
- ❏ Zookeepers (3)

FIND BUNNY HONEY
AT THE
COSTUME PARTY
AND...

- ❏ Apple
- ❏ Arrow
- ❏ Barrel
- ❏ Basket
- ❏ Beaver
- ❏ Bells (2)
- ❏ Broom
- ❏ Cactus (2)
- ❏ Clothespin
- ❏ Coffeepot
- ❏ Crown
- ❏ Ear of corn
- ❏ Egg
- ❏ Football
- ❏ Fork
- ❏ Frog
- ❏ Headless dancer
- ❏ Hot dog
- ❏ Ice-cream pop
- ❏ Ice skate
- ❏ Kite
- ❏ Lollipop
- ❏ Magnifying glass
- ❏ Pencils (2)
- ❏ Pizza
- ❏ Roller skates
- ❏ Skateboards (2)
- ❏ Tepee
- ❏ Yellow birds (2)

FIND BUNNY HONEY
AT THE
FACTORY
AND...

- ❑ Apple
- ❑ Arrow
- ❑ Baseball bat
- ❑ Basketball
- ❑ Birds (6)
- ❑ Black jelly beans (3)
- ❑ Candle
- ❑ Carrot
- ❑ Chimney
- ❑ Clothespins (2)
- ❑ Fish
- ❑ Flower
- ❑ Football player
- ❑ Handbag
- ❑ Igloo
- ❑ Knight
- ❑ Lost shoe
- ❑ Monster
- ❑ Pencil
- ❑ Pig
- ❑ Referee
- ❑ Snake
- ❑ Spear
- ❑ Top hat
- ❑ Turtle
- ❑ Umbrella
- ❑ Vacuum cleaner
- ❑ Worm
- ❑ Zebra

FIND BUNNY HONEY

AT THE

HONEY BUNNY HOTEL

AND...

- ❏ Balloons (3)
- ❏ Basketball
- ❏ Bowling ball
- ❏ Burned-out light
- ❏ Cactus
- ❏ Carrots (3)
- ❏ Chef
- ❏ Crack in egg
- ❏ Diving board
- ❏ Elephant
- ❏ Fish
- ❏ Frog
- ❏ Giraffe
- ❏ Jack-o'-lantern
- ❏ Ladders (3)
- ❏ Lifeguard
- ❏ Mouse
- ❏ Painter
- ❏ Parachute
- ❏ Periscope
- ❏ Pole vaulter
- ❏ Santa bunny
- ❏ Scarecrow
- ❏ Skateboard
- ❏ Snake
- ❏ Star
- ❏ Telescope
- ❏ Tree
- ❏ Yellow birds (4)

FIND BUNNY HONEY
AT THE
GREAT EGG ROLL
AND...

- ☐ Ant
- ☐ Bee
- ☐ Clothespin
- ☐ Dogs (2)
- ☐ Duck
- ☐ Elephant
- ☐ Feather
- ☐ Fish
- ☐ Flamingo
- ☐ Football
- ☐ Fried egg
- ☐ Frog
- ☐ Helmet
- ☐ Horse
- ☐ Kangaroo
- ☐ Kite
- ☐ Magnifying glass
- ☐ Meatballs
- ☐ Paintbrush
- ☐ Raccoon
- ☐ Rhinoceros
- ☐ Scarves (2)
- ☐ Seal
- ☐ Skateboard
- ☐ Snake
- ☐ Spaceship
- ☐ Sunglasses
- ☐ Top hat
- ☐ Toucan
- ☐ Walrus

FIND BUNNY HONEY
AT THE
SPRING SALE
AND...

- ❑ Arrow
- ❑ Astronaut
- ❑ Banana peel
- ❑ Basket
- ❑ Birdcage
- ❑ Boxing glove
- ❑ Cactus
- ❑ Candle
- ❑ Centipede
- ❑ Chef
- ❑ Clothespin
- ❑ Clown
- ❑ Crown
- ❑ Fishing pole
- ❑ Flowerpot
- ❑ Ghost
- ❑ Horse
- ❑ Humpty Dumpty
- ❑ Igloo
- ❑ Lamp
- ❑ Monkey
- ❑ Mouse
- ❑ Octopus
- ❑ Owl
- ❑ Pies (2)
- ❑ Pirate
- ❑ Police officer
- ❑ Rooster
- ❑ Sailor hat
- ❑ Shopping bags (3)
- ❑ Sofa

FIND BUNNY HONEY

IN FAIRY-TALE LAND AND...

- ❏ Arrow
- ❏ Banana peel
- ❏ Bell
- ❏ Broom
- ❏ Bucket
- ❏ Cactus
- ❏ Candle
- ❏ Comb
- ❏ Cooking pot
- ❏ Dog
- ❏ Earring
- ❏ Firecracker
- ❏ Golf club
- ❏ Hearts (2)
- ❏ "Ho-ho-ho!"
- ❏ Kangaroo
- ❏ Moose
- ❏ Muffin man
- ❏ Painted egg
- ❏ Paper bag
- ❏ Saw
- ❏ Screwdriver
- ❏ Seesaw
- ❏ Shovel
- ❏ Slipper
- ❏ Sneakers
- ❏ Star
- ❏ Toothbrush
- ❏ Umbrellas (3)

FIND BUNNY
HONEY
AT THE
SNOWMAN
MELTDOWN
AND...

- ❏ Baseball
- ❏ Birds (4)
- ❏ Broom
- ❏ Butterfly
- ❏ Cage
- ❏ Candy cane
- ❏ Clown
- ❏ Drum
- ❏ Duck
- ❏ Fire hydrant
- ❏ Ghost
- ❏ Hammer
- ❏ Heart
- ❏ Hockey puck
- ❏ Jack-o'-lantern
- ❏ Key
- ❏ Kite
- ❏ Lollipop
- ❏ Milk container
- ❏ Pig
- ❏ Roller skater
- ❏ Rooster
- ❏ Sleeping cat
- ❏ Sock
- ❏ Stars (2)
- ❏ Sunglasses (2)
- ❏ Worm
- ❏ Wreath

FIND BUNNY HONEY
IN THIS
ZANY EGG CONTEST
AND...

- ❏ Arrow
- ❏ Balloon
- ❏ Bear
- ❏ Books (3)
- ❏ Cat
- ❏ Chick
- ❏ Cup
- ❏ Dog
- ❏ Fallen leaf
- ❏ Feather
- ❏ Fish
- ❏ Flowerpot
- ❏ Flying bat
- ❏ Frying pan
- ❏ Ghost
- ❏ Horseshoe
- ❏ Key
- ❏ Kite
- ❏ Magnifying glass
- ❏ Neckties (2)
- ❏ Paper airplane
- ❏ Pencil
- ❏ Star
- ❏ Toothbrush
- ❏ Tree stump
- ❏ Turtle
- ❏ Zebra

DETECT DONALD IN COLONIAL AMERICA AND...

DETECT
DONALD
IN THE
FUTURE
AND...

- Apple
- Cactus
- Christmas ornament
- Clock
- Ear
- Elephant
- Evergreen tree
- Fish
- Football
- Football helmet
- Graduate's hat
- Guitar
- Ice-cream cone
- Ice skate
- Jester
- Key
- Nail
- Paintbrush
- Postage stamp
- Roller skate
- Santa Claus
- Skateboard
- Snowman
- Spoon
- Stop sign
- Tepee
- Watering can

DETECT DONALD IN THE MIDDLE AGES AND...

DETECT DONALD AT THE PIRATES' BATTLE AND...

DETECT DONALD IN NAPOLEON'S FRANCE AND...

DETECT DONALD
IN
ANCIENT ROME
AND...

- ❏ Arrow
- ❏ Backwards helmet
- ❏ Balloon
- ❏ Cactus
- ❏ Caesar
- ❏ Cat
- ❏ Falling rock
- ❏ Flower
- ❏ Horseless chariot
- ❏ Jack-o'-lantern
- ❏ Julius and Augustus
- ❏ Kite
- ❏ Mask
- ❏ Painted egg
- ❏ Pig
- ❏ Pizza box
- ❏ Puddles (2)
- ❏ Rabbit
- ❏ Shield
- ❏ Skull
- ❏ Slice of pizza
- ❏ Snake
- ❏ Sock
- ❏ Spears (2)
- ❏ Star
- ❏ Underwear

DETECT DONALD

IN

PREHISTORIC TIMES

AND...

- ❏ Blue hats (3)
- ❏ Briefcase
- ❏ Broom
- ❏ Car
- ❏ Cave
- ❏ Crown
- ❏ Football
- ❏ Glass pitcher
- ❏ Guitar
- ❏ Kite
- ❏ Lasso
- ❏ Lion
- ❏ Logs (2)
- ❏ Lunch box
- ❏ Periscope
- ❏ Pig
- ❏ Pink flamingo
- ❏ Red bows (4)
- ❏ Snakes (3)
- ❏ Soccer ball
- ❏ Spoon
- ❏ Stone axe
- ❏ Superhero
- ❏ Tin man
- ❏ Tire
- ❏ Trumpet
- ❏ Volcano

DETECT DONALD AT THE ACADEMY AWARDS AND...

HUNT FOR HECTOR
AT THE
SUPER DOG BOWL
AND...

HUNT FOR HECTOR
AT
DOG SCHOOL
AND...

HUNT FOR HECTOR
AMONG THE
DOGCATCHERS
AND...

- ❏ Airplane
- ❏ Barber pole
- ❏ Bathing dog
- ❏ Briefcase
- ❏ Car antenna
- ❏ Cats (5)
- ❏ Convertible car
- ❏ Dog bowls (3)
- ❏ "Dog mail"
- ❏ Dollar signs (11)
- ❏ Empty bowls (2)
- ❏ Fire hose
- ❏ Fire hydrants (4)
- ❏ Fire truck
- ❏ Fishing pole
- ❏ Guitar
- ❏ Heart
- ❏ Manhole
- ❏ Musical note
- ❏ Net
- ❏ Piano
- ❏ Pink hats (8)
- ❏ Rope swing
- ❏ Satellite dish
- ❏ Shower
- ❏ Sirens (2)
- ❏ Tree
- ❏ Turtle
- ❏ "UDS"
- ❏ Umbrella
- ❏ Watermelon
- ❏ Water tower

HUNT FOR HECTOR
WHERE THE
RICH AND
FAMOUS DOGS
LIVE
AND...

- ❏ Admiral
- ❏ Alligator
- ❏ Artist
- ❏ "Big Wheel"
- ❏ Bird bath
- ❏ Blimp
- ❏ Bone chimney
- ❏ Candle
- ❏ Castle
- ❏ Cat
- ❏ Cooks (2)
- ❏ Crown
- ❏ Dog fish
- ❏ Dog flag
- ❏ Fire hydrant
- ❏ Golfers (2)
- ❏ Guard
- ❏ Heart
- ❏ Heron
- ❏ Human
- ❏ Joggers (3)
- ❏ Periscope
- ❏ Pillow
- ❏ Pool
- ❏ Sipping a soda
- ❏ Star
- ❏ Tennis player
- ❏ Umbrella
- ❏ Violinist
- ❏ Water skier
- ❏ Whale

HUNT FOR HECTOR
AT THE
K-9
CLEAN UP
AND...

- ❏ Anchor
- ❏ Bones (2)
- ❏ Broken piggy bank
- ❏ Butterfly net
- ❏ Cane
- ❏ Chimney
- ❏ "Chow" bowl
- ❏ Cowboy hat
- ❏ Doorbell
- ❏ Duck
- ❏ Fake mustache
- ❏ Feather
- ❏ Fire hose
- ❏ Fire hydrants (3)
- ❏ Fishing pole
- ❏ Helicopter
- ❏ "K-9" helmet
- ❏ Manhole cover
- ❏ Motorcycle
- ❏ Pails of water (7)
- ❏ Parachute
- ❏ Penguin
- ❏ Rope ladder
- ❏ Rowboat
- ❏ Sailor's hat
- ❏ Scrub brush
- ❏ Skateboard
- ❏ "S.S. Poseidon"
- ❏ Superpooch
- ❏ Tin cans (4)

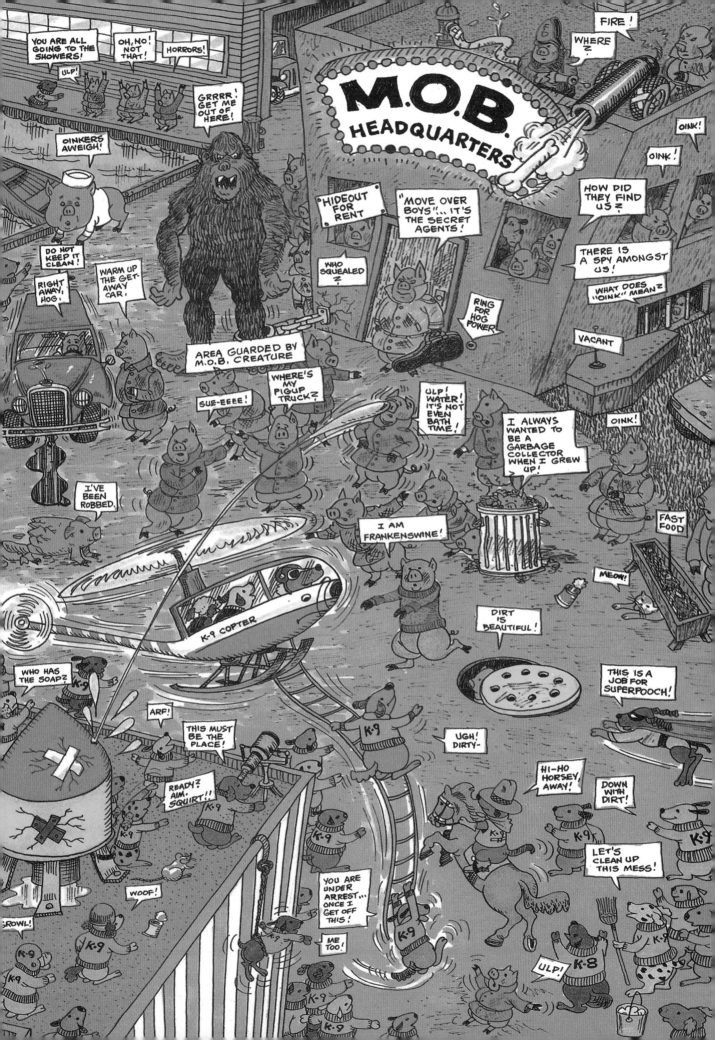

HUNT FOR HECTOR
AT THE
DOG MALL
AND...

- ☐ Air conditioner
- ☐ Barber's pole
- ☐ Baseball
- ☐ Bone cake
- ☐ "Bone on a Bun"
- ☐ Bookstore
- ☐ Car
- ☐ Cats (2)
- ☐ Chef's hat
- ☐ Clown
- ☐ Cookies (2)
- ☐ Crooked chimney
- ☐ Doghouse
- ☐ Dog in shining armor
- ☐ Fire hydrants (2)
- ☐ "Food Court"
- ☐ "For Rent"
- ☐ Graduate
- ☐ Hockey stick
- ☐ "Hunk" poster
- ☐ Leashes (3)
- ☐ Lollipop
- ☐ Mug
- ☐ Newspaper seller
- ☐ Paper airplane
- ☐ Scissors
- ☐ Spotlight
- ☐ Suitcase
- ☐ Trophy
- ☐ Turkey
- ☐ Witch dog

HUNT FOR HECTOR
AT THE
TV QUIZ SHOW
AND...

HUNT FOR HECTOR IN SPACE AND...

- ❏ Bench
- ❏ Blimp
- ❏ Boat
- ❏ Bone antenna
- ❏ Bone smokestack
- ❏ Boxing glove
- ❏ Bus
- ❏ Cars (3)
- ❏ Diving board
- ❏ "Dog fish"
- ❏ Dog in trash can
- ❏ "Dog paddle"
- ❏ Earth
- ❏ Emergency dog
- ❏ Graduate dog
- ❏ Heart with arrow
- ❏ Hot dog
- ❏ Juggler
- ❏ Mailbag
- ❏ Nut
- ❏ Old tire
- ❏ Pirate
- ❏ Pizza
- ❏ Pluto
- ❏ Pup in a cup
- ❏ Roller coaster
- ❏ Space map
- ❏ Star with tail
- ❏ Top hat
- ❏ UFO
- ❏ Unicycle
- ❏ Vampire dog

HUNT FOR HECTOR
IN
DOGTOWN
AND...

- ☐ Baby carriage
- ☐ Barbecue
- ☐ "Bark Your Horn"
- ☐ Basketball
- ☐ Bicycle
- ☐ Birds (2)
- ☐ Boat
- ☐ Crossing guard
- ☐ "Dog cookies"
- ☐ Dog fountain
- ☐ Falling "G"
- ☐ Gas pump
- ☐ Hammer
- ☐ Hard hats (3)
- ☐ Human on leash
- ☐ Lawn mower
- ☐ Mailbox
- ☐ Manhole
- ☐ Piano
- ☐ Pool
- ☐ Sailor
- ☐ Santa Claus
- ☐ Screwdriver
- ☐ Skateboard
- ☐ Soccer ball
- ☐ Sock
- ☐ Streetlight
- ☐ Super Dog
- ☐ Swimming pool
- ☐ Trash cans (2)
- ☐ TV
- ☐ Wrench

LOOK FOR LISA AT THE MARATHON AND...

- ☐ Angel
- ☐ Barrel
- ☐ Basketball
- ☐ Bucket
- ☐ Cane
- ☐ Chef
- ☐ Cowboy
- ☐ Deer
- ☐ Diving board
- ☐ Doctor
- ☐ Elephants (2)
- ☐ Ice-cream cone
- ☐ Kite
- ☐ Motorcycle
- ☐ Musical notes (3)
- ☐ Net
- ☐ Octopus
- ☐ Periscope
- ☐ Policeman
- ☐ Rocket
- ☐ Roller skates
- ☐ Sad face
- ☐ Scooter
- ☐ "Shortcut"
- ☐ Sombrero
- ☐ Speed skater
- ☐ Spotted dog
- ☐ Strongman
- ☐ Surfer
- ☐ Taxi
- ☐ Tuba
- ☐ Umbrella

LOOK FOR LISA AT THE ROCK CONCERT AND...

- ❏ Alien
- ❏ Balloons (6)
- ❏ Barbell
- ❏ Bowling ball
- ❏ Crown
- ❏ Doctor
- ❏ Fish tank
- ❏ Flamingo
- ❏ Flowers
- ❏ Hot dog stand
- ❏ Knight
- ❏ Lamppost
- ❏ Masked man
- ❏ Moon
- ❏ Mummy
- ❏ Net
- ❏ Painter
- ❏ Prisoner
- ❏ Rabbit
- ❏ Snowman
- ❏ Stack of pizza boxes
- ❏ Stars (6)
- ❏ Tin man
- ❏ Tombstones (2)
- ❏ Trampoline
- ❏ Viking
- ❏ Waiter
- ❏ Witch
- ❏ Zebra

LOOK FOR LISA
AT THE
BEACH
AND...

- ❏ Artist
- ❏ Beach ball
- ❏ Broom
- ❏ Bunch of balloons
- ❏ Cactus (4)
- ❏ Castle
- ❏ Cello
- ❏ Crocodile
- ❏ Cruise ship
- ❏ Diving board
- ❏ Hearts (3)
- ❏ Horse
- ❏ Jack-in-the-box
- ❏ Kite
- ❏ Lifeguard
- ❏ Lost swim trunks
- ❏ Magnifying glass
- ❏ Merman
- ❏ Palm trees (3)
- ❏ Pickle barrel
- ❏ Policeman
- ❏ Sailboat
- ❏ Sailors (2)
- ❏ Sea serpent
- ❏ Seahorse
- ❏ Starfish (9)
- ❏ Swans (2)
- ❏ Telescope
- ❏ Trash can
- ❏ Tricycle
- ❏ Turtle
- ❏ Whale

LOOK FOR LISA
AT THE
LIBRARY
AND...

- ❏ Baseball
- ❏ Birdcage
- ❏ Bowling pins (10)
- ❏ Brooms (2)
- ❏ Cactus
- ❏ Cactus book
- ❏ Cake
- ❏ Campfire
- ❏ Candle
- ❏ Car
- ❏ Football player
- ❏ Frying pan
- ❏ Globe
- ❏ Hamburger
- ❏ Hearts (4)
- ❏ Hockey stick
- ❏ Hot dog
- ❏ Jack-in-the-box
- ❏ Knight
- ❏ Monster hands (3)
- ❏ Musical note
- ❏ Napoleon
- ❏ Old tire
- ❏ Pole-vaulter
- ❏ Policewoman
- ❏ "Quiet" signs (6)
- ❏ Smiley face
- ❏ Teapot
- ❏ Trap door
- ❏ Tricycle
- ❏ Wagon
- ❏ Witch

LOOK FOR LISA AT THE AMUSEMENT PARK AND...

- ❏ All North
- ❏ Weather vane
- ❏ Archer
- ❏ Cheese
- ❏ Clock
- ❏ Clowns (3)
- ❏ Cowboys (2)
- ❏ Crocodile
- ❏ Crooked chimney
- ❏ Diving board
- ❏ Dollar sign
- ❏ Fishing pole
- ❏ Heads without bodies (2)
- ❏ Ice block
- ❏ Manhole
- ❏ Moon
- ❏ Mouse hole
- ❏ Mummy
- ❏ Pear
- ❏ Snowman
- ❏ Space explorer
- ❏ Tent
- ❏ Tied-up man
- ❏ Tin man
- ❏ Tombstones (3)
- ❏ "Tunnel of Love"
- ❏ Umbrella
- ❏ Witch
- ❏ Wristwatches (7)

LOOK FOR LISA
AS THE
CIRCUS COMES TO TOWN
AND...

- ❏ Aliens (2)
- ❏ Barbell
- ❏ Bass drum
- ❏ Bone
- ❏ Broom
- ❏ Camel
- ❏ Cowboys (4)
- ❏ Crown
- ❏ "Enter"
- ❏ Flags (7)
- ❏ Frankenstein's monster
- ❏ Hole
- ❏ Juggler
- ❏ Musical note
- ❏ Net
- ❏ Plates (7)
- ❏ Police officers (2)
- ❏ Poodle
- ❏ Rabbit
- ❏ Sad face
- ❏ Soldiers (2)
- ❏ Stroller
- ❏ Tin man
- ❏ Turtle
- ❏ Unicorn
- ❏ Unicycle
- ❏ Whistle
- ❏ Witch

LOOK FOR LISA IN THESE CAVERNOUS CRATERS AND...

- ❏ Axe
- ❏ Banana
- ❏ Bucket
- ❏ Car
- ❏ Clown
- ❏ Coffeepot
- ❏ Cup
- ❏ Duck
- ❏ Earth
- ❏ Envelope
- ❏ Fish
- ❏ Flashlight
- ❏ Heart
- ❏ Key
- ❏ Kite
- ❏ Ladder
- ❏ Mouse
- ❏ Penguin
- ❏ Pig
- ❏ Pumpkin
- ❏ Ring
- ❏ Saw
- ❏ Shovel
- ❏ Stamp
- ❏ Stars (4)
- ❏ Stool
- ❏ Toothbrush
- ❏ Turtle

LOOK FOR LISA
IN THE
OCEAN
AND...

- ❏ Baby
- ❏ Barrel
- ❏ Baseball bat
- ❏ Basketball
- ❏ Boot
- ❏ Bucket
- ❏ Captain's hat
- ❏ Elephant
- ❏ Fish (3)
- ❏ Guitar
- ❏ Harp
- ❏ Heart
- ❏ Homework
- ❏ Hot-air balloon
- ❏ Ice-cream cone
- ❏ Key
- ❏ Oars (5)
- ❏ Painting
- ❏ Palm tree
- ❏ Scuba diver
- ❏ Shark fins (2)
- ❏ Slice of watermelon
- ❏ Sock
- ❏ Surfer
- ❏ Television
- ❏ Tin can
- ❏ Tire
- ❏ Tree

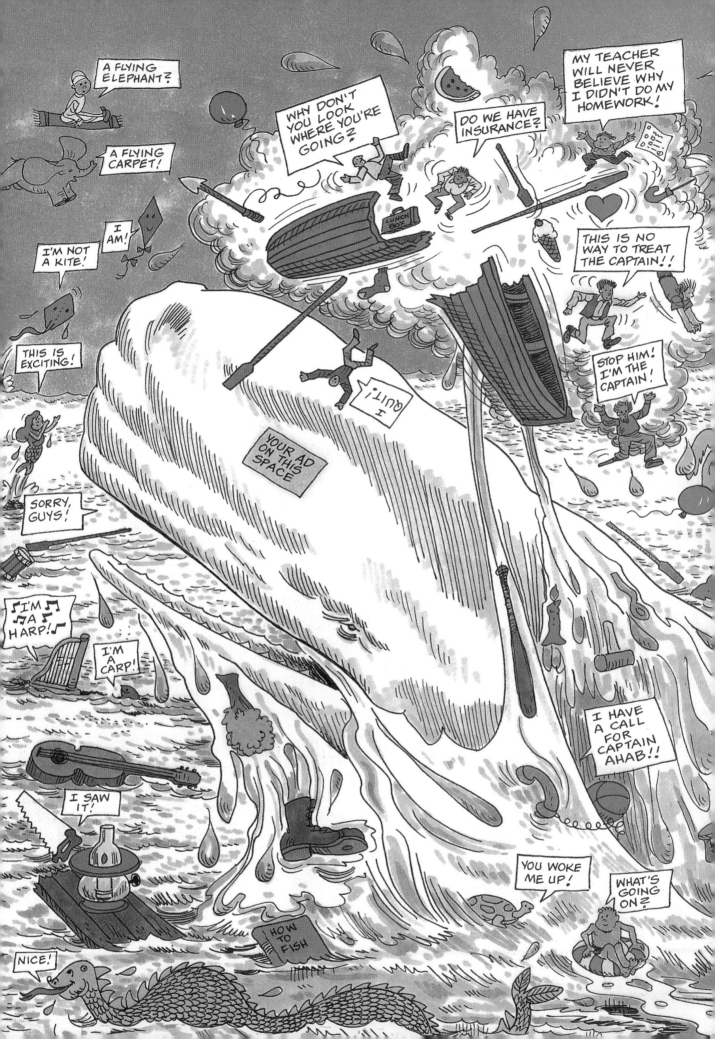

LOOK
FOR LISA
AT THE
MAGIC SHOW
AND...

- ❏ Apple
- ❏ Barbell
- ❏ Barrel
- ❏ Beard
- ❏ Box
- ❏ Burned-out
  light bulbs (2)
- ❏ Dragon
- ❏ Elephants (2)
- ❏ Football
- ❏ Graduation cap
- ❏ Headband
- ❏ Heart
- ❏ Jack-o'-lantern
- ❏ Key
- ❏ Knight
- ❏ Leaf
- ❏ Mouse
- ❏ Palm tree
- ❏ Puppy
- ❏ Purple hat
- ❏ Rabbit
- ❏ Sandbag
- ❏ Snake
- ❏ Top hat
- ❏ Trapdoors (2)
- ❏ Weightlifter
- ❏ Whale

LOOK FOR LISA
AS SHE
ROCKS
AND ROLLS
AND...

- ❏ Accordion
- ❏ Bandana
- ❏ Bow tie
- ❏ Broken nose
- ❏ Cameras (5)
- ❏ Cymbals
- ❏ Earmuffs
- ❏ Elephant
- ❏ Feather
- ❏ Fiddle
- ❏ Flags (2)
- ❏ Flying bat
- ❏ Football helmet
- ❏ Harmonica
- ❏ Horse
- ❏ King Kong
- ❏ Ladder
- ❏ Mailbox
- ❏ Microphones (2)
- ❏ Paper airplane
- ❏ Propeller hat
- ❏ Red wagon
- ❏ Scarf
- ❏ Speaker
- ❏ Stage lights (6)
- ❏ Submarine
- ❏ Trumpet
- ❏ Turtle

SEARCH FOR SYLVESTER AS HE SOARS THROUGH THE SKYGROUND AND...

- ❑ Ape
- ❑ Banana
- ❑ Baseball bat
- ❑ Bathtub
- ❑ Bird
- ❑ Bow
- ❑ Carrot
- ❑ Cupcake
- ❑ Fishermen (2)
- ❑ Flowers (4)
- ❑ Flying bat
- ❑ Football player
- ❑ Guitar
- ❑ Moon
- ❑ Pot
- ❑ Scarecrow
- ❑ Scarf
- ❑ Shovel
- ❑ Spaceship
- ❑ Stars (3)
- ❑ Sunglasses
- ❑ Target
- ❑ Teapot
- ❑ Tent
- ❑ TV antenna
- ❑ Watering can
- ❑ Witch

SEARCH FOR SYLVESTER AT FAST FOOD HEAVEN AND...

- ☐ Alligator
- ☐ Bone
- ☐ Bowling ball
- ☐ Carrot
- ☐ Club
- ☐ Crowns (2)
- ☐ Dogs (2)
- ☐ Drum
- ☐ Elf
- ☐ Flying bat
- ☐ Football player
- ☐ Frog
- ☐ Ice-cream cone
- ☐ Jack-o'-lantern
- ☐ Jogger
- ☐ Kite
- ☐ Mouse
- ☐ Owl
- ☐ Pickle
- ☐ Popped balloon
- ☐ Rabbit
- ☐ Shopping bag
- ☐ Skier
- ☐ Snowman
- ☐ Tire
- ☐ Trees (2)
- ☐ Tugboat
- ☐ Turtle
- ☐ Witch
- ☐ Worm

SEARCH FOR SYLVESTER

AT THE

ZANY ZOO

AND...

- ❏ Baseball bat
- ❏ Baseball caps (4)
- ❏ Bow tie
- ❏ Camel
- ❏ Fish
- ❏ Football
- ❏ Girl with pigtails
- ❏ Kangaroo
- ❏ Little Red Riding Hood
- ❏ Neckties (3)
- ❏ Owl
- ❏ Parrot
- ❏ Pig
- ❏ Pine tree
- ❏ Rabbit
- ❏ Raccoon
- ❏ Scarf
- ❏ School bus
- ❏ Sea horse
- ❏ Seal
- ❏ Shovel
- ❏ Spoon
- ❏ Telescope
- ❏ Top hat
- ❏ Toy turtle
- ❏ Trash can
- ❏ Turtle
- ❏ Waiter

SEARCH FOR SYLVESTER AT THIS SPOOKY MANSION AND...

- ❏ Arrows (2)
- ❏ Book
- ❏ Brush
- ❏ Bucket
- ❏ Candle
- ❏ Carrot
- ❏ Cauldron
- ❏ Curtains
- ❏ Flower
- ❏ Flying bat
- ❏ Football
- ❏ Ghost
- ❏ Hammer
- ❏ Lawn mower
- ❏ Letter
- ❏ Old tire
- ❏ Piano keys
- ❏ Shovel
- ❏ Skulls (2)
- ❏ Spiderweb
- ❏ Sword
- ❏ Tin can
- ❏ Trash can lid
- ❏ Vulture
- ❏ Wagon
- ❏ Watering can
- ❏ Witch

SEARCH FOR SYLVESTER AT DETECTIVE DONALD'S DIGS AND...

- ❏ Broken pencils (3)
- ❏ Calendar
- ❏ Can
- ❏ Candles (3)
- ❏ Chalk
- ❏ Chalkboard
- ❏ Cheese
- ❏ Comb
- ❏ Diploma
- ❏ Fan
- ❏ Fishing pole
- ❏ Jacket
- ❏ Key
- ❏ Ladder
- ❏ Lamp
- ❏ Medal
- ❏ Nail
- ❏ Paint bucket
- ❏ Roller skate
- ❏ Screwdriver
- ❏ Shovel
- ❏ Skull
- ❏ Snake
- ❏ Stack of envelopes
- ❏ Sword
- ❏ Tack
- ❏ Top hat
- ❏ Trunk

SEARCH FOR SYLVESTER
AT THIS
SILLY CIRCUS
AND...

- ❏ Balloon with star
- ❏ Barrel
- ❏ Cactus
- ❏ Cake
- ❏ Camel
- ❏ Cannon
- ❏ Clothespins (3)
- ❏ Clowns (4)
- ❏ Crayon
- ❏ Firefighter
- ❏ Flowerpot
- ❏ Light bulb
- ❏ Mice (2)
- ❏ Necktie
- ❏ Party hat
- ❏ Pinocchio
- ❏ Pizza
- ❏ Police officer
- ❏ Skateboard
- ❏ Snowman
- ❏ Spoon
- ❏ Stars (5)
- ❏ Teacup
- ❏ Tin man
- ❏ Unicycle
- ❏ Witch
- ❏ Wizard hat
- ❏ Worm

SEARCH FOR SYLVESTER

IN

BAMBOO TOWN

AND...

- ☐ Balloons (2)
- ☐ Brooms (2)
- ☐ Drum
- ☐ Eyeglasses (2)
- ☐ Fire hydrants (2)
- ☐ Football
- ☐ Football player
- ☐ Ghost
- ☐ Gift
- ☐ Hard hats (2)
- ☐ Heart
- ☐ Horseshoe
- ☐ Ice-cream cones (2)
- ☐ Jump rope
- ☐ Kangaroo
- ☐ Knight
- ☐ Mask
- ☐ Medal
- ☐ Octopus
- ☐ Pencil
- ☐ Periscope
- ☐ Record
- ☐ Socks (3)
- ☐ Stool
- ☐ Straw
- ☐ Telescope
- ☐ Wizard
- ☐ Worm

FIND WENDY
AT
WITCHVILLE HIGH SCHOOL
AND...

- ❏ Apple
- ❏ Axe
- ❏ Baseball bat
- ❏ Bear
- ❏ Bell
- ❏ Blimp
- ❏ Bowling ball
- ❏ Cauldrons (2)
- ❏ Dog
- ❏ Flying bats (2)
- ❏ Football
- ❏ Green hand
- ❏ Headless man
- ❏ Mask
- ❏ Mushrooms (3)
- ❏ One-eyed monsters (2)
- ❏ Pencil
- ❏ Piece of paper
- ❏ Scarecrow
- ❏ Shovel
- ❏ Skateboard
- ❏ Tire
- ❏ Tombstones (3)
- ❏ Turtle
- ❏ TV antenna
- ❏ Unicorn
- ❏ Walking tree
- ❏ Worm

FIND WENDY
IN THE
LUNCHROOM
AND...

- ❏ Apple
- ❏ Bird
- ❏ Broken nose
- ❏ Cactus
- ❏ Candle
- ❏ Cat
- ❏ Chick
- ❏ Cookbook
- ❏ Crystal ball
- ❏ Cymbals (2)
- ❏ Drum
- ❏ Flower
- ❏ Football
- ❏ Frying pans (3)
- ❏ Graduate
- ❏ Lighthouse
- ❏ Musical notes (3)
- ❏ Paper airplane
- ❏ Plate of cookies
- ❏ Santa Claus
- ❏ Skull
- ❏ Snakes (2)
- ❏ Straw
- ❏ Teapot
- ❏ Trash can
- ❏ Turtle
- ❏ Volcano
- ❏ Yellow hand
- ❏ Yellow sock

FIND WENDY
DURING
FINAL EXAMS
AND...

FIND WENDY
AT
GRADUATION
AND...

- ☐ Barbell
- ☐ Bones (2)
- ☐ Broken mirror
- ☐ Brooms (3)
- ☐ Can
- ☐ Candle
- ☐ Cracked egg
- ☐ Dog
- ☐ Drum
- ☐ Flying bats (2)
- ☐ Ghost
- ☐ Graduation cap
- ☐ Guitar
- ☐ Kite
- ☐ Marshmallow
- ☐ Moons (2)
- ☐ Musical note
- ☐ Panda
- ☐ Pumpkins (2)
- ☐ Robot
- ☐ Sled
- ☐ Target
- ☐ Tire
- ☐ Tombstones (13)
- ☐ Toolbox
- ☐ Turtle
- ☐ Umbrella
- ☐ Wizard
- ☐ Worm

FIND WENDY
IN THE
MUMMY'S
TOMB
AND...

SO YOU WANT
TO BE A
STAR-A-SAURUS

FIND THESE ITEMS...

- ❏ Beret
- ❏ Bird
- ❏ Bottle
- ❏ Bow ties (2)
- ❏ Box
- ❏ Candle
- ❏ Clipboard
- ❏ Crown
- ❏ Dracula-saurus
- ❏ Drum
- ❏ Flower
- ❏ Fork
- ❏ Frying pan
- ❏ Ghost
- ❏ Heart
- ❏ Medal
- ❏ Mustaches (2)
- ❏ Pearl necklace
- ❏ Pencils (2)
- ❏ Periscope
- ❏ Pointy beards (2)
- ❏ Scarves (3)
- ❏ Stars (2)
- ❏ Sunglasses (3)
- ❏ Sword
- ❏ Ten-gallon hat
- ❏ Ticket
- ❏ Tic-tac-toe
- ❏ Top hat
- ❏ Walking stick

MARATHON-A-SAURUS

FIND THESE ITEMS...

- ❑ Automobile
- ❑ Axe
- ❑ Bird
- ❑ Bowling ball
- ❑ Cactus
- ❑ Cell phone
- ❑ Coffeepot
- ❑ Cup
- ❑ Fire hydrant
- ❑ Fish
- ❑ Jack-o'-lantern
- ❑ Jester's cap
- ❑ Key
- ❑ Kite
- ❑ Lost baseball caps (2)
- ❑ Moustache
- ❑ Pencil
- ❑ Rolling pin
- ❑ Skateboard
- ❑ Socks (2)
- ❑ Star
- ❑ Straw
- ❑ Telescope
- ❑ Tent
- ❑ Traffic light
- ❑ Tulip
- ❑ Turtle
- ❑ Volcano

THE FAMOUS STORY OF FRANKENSAURUS

FIND THESE ITEMS...

- Alarm clock
- Axe
- Banana peel
- Band-Aids (2)
- Baseball bat
- Baseball cap
- Bow and arrow
- Bowling ball
- Candle
- Cupcake
- Dead flower
- Drum
- Eyeglasses
- Fire hydrant
- Fish
- Football
- Heart
- Knitting needles
- Lollipop
- Oil can
- Paddle
- Paper airplane
- Pencils (2)
- Periscope
- Pizza
- Rolling pin
- Saw
- Scissors
- Screwdriver
- Sunglasses
- Tape
- Thermometer
- Tic-tac-toe
- Turtle
- Yo-yo

DINO WRESTLING IS REALLY HUGE!

FIND THESE ITEMS...

- ❑ Band-Aid
- ❑ Baseball caps (3)
- ❑ Baseball glove
- ❑ Basketball
- ❑ Bow tie
- ❑ Camera
- ❑ Drinking straw
- ❑ Egg
- ❑ Envelope
- ❑ Flowers
- ❑ Harmonica
- ❑ Headphones (2)
- ❑ Heart
- ❑ Hot dog
- ❑ Ice-cream cone
- ❑ Kite
- ❑ Lost balloons (2)
- ❑ Microphone
- ❑ Necktie
- ❑ Pencils (2)
- ❑ Periscope
- ❑ Scarf
- ❑ Slice of pizza
- ❑ Straw hat
- ❑ Sunglasses
- ❑ Telescope
- ❑ Top hat
- ❑ Yo-yo

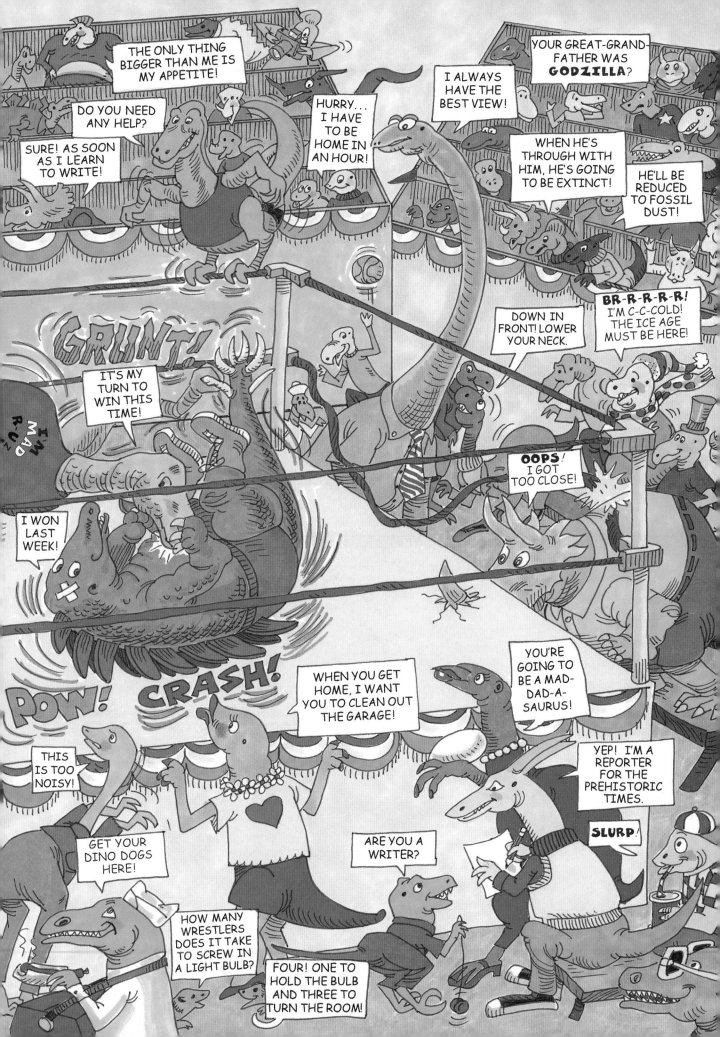

DINOSAURS
IN
SPACE

FIND THESE ITEMS...

- ❏ Apple
- ❏ Banana
- ❏ Band-Aid
- ❏ Barber pole
- ❏ Baseball
- ❏ Baseball cap
- ❏ Bow tie
- ❏ Cane
- ❏ Carrot
- ❏ Coffeepot
- ❏ Cups (2)
- ❏ Envelopes (2)
- ❏ Flower pot
- ❏ Garden hose
- ❏ Hammer
- ❏ Hitchhiker
- ❏ Ice-cream cone
- ❏ Key
- ❏ Kite
- ❏ Lost shoe
- ❏ Medal
- ❏ Oil can
- ❏ Pencil
- ❏ Saw
- ❏ Screwdriver
- ❏ Shovel
- ❏ Speaker
- ❏ Telescope
- ❏ Tepee
- ❏ Tic-tac-toe
- ❏ Toothbrush

DINOSAUR VACATIONS IN NEW YORK CITY

FIND THESE ITEMS...

- ❑ Banana
- ❑ Bicycle messenger
- ❑ Bone
- ❑ Burned-out bulbs (3)
- ❑ Camera
- ❑ Cane
- ❑ Clipboard
- ❑ Clothespin
- ❑ Crayon
- ❑ Envelope
- ❑ Fire hydrants (3)
- ❑ Fork
- ❑ Ghost
- ❑ Hearts (2)
- ❑ Horseshoe
- ❑ Ice-cream cone
- ❑ In-line skater
- ❑ Jack-o'-lantern
- ❑ Ladder
- ❑ Lost balloon
- ❑ Mouse
- ❑ Paintbrush
- ❑ Paper airplane
- ❑ Party hat
- ❑ Tepee
- ❑ Worm

DINOSAURS IN KING ARTHUR'S COURT

FIND THESE ITEMS...

- ☐ Balloon
- ☐ Banana
- ☐ Banana peels (2)
- ☐ Baseball cap
- ☐ Basketball
- ☐ Bell
- ☐ Bird
- ☐ Bone
- ☐ Bow tie
- ☐ Candle
- ☐ Carrot
- ☐ Clothespins (3)
- ☐ Earring
- ☐ Feather
- ☐ Ice-cream cone
- ☐ Jestersaurus
- ☐ Jugglesaurus
- ☐ Light bulb
- ☐ Merlinasaurus
- ☐ Pearl necklace
- ☐ Roller skate
- ☐ Sock
- ☐ Swords (3)
- ☐ Telescope
- ☐ Whale

DINOSAURS
IN A
WILD WEST TOWN

FIND THESE ITEMS...

- ❏ Arrows (2)
- ❏ Axe
- ❏ Badges (2)
- ❏ Balloons (2)
- ❏ Banana
- ❏ Barrel
- ❏ Bones (2)
- ❏ Bow tie
- ❏ Brush
- ❏ Cactus (2)
- ❏ Candle
- ❏ Cheese
- ❏ Coonskin caps (2)
- ❏ Cup
- ❏ Drums (2)
- ❏ Elephant
- ❏ Eyeglasses
- ❏ Fire hydrant
- ❏ Fish
- ❏ Flower
- ❏ Football
- ❏ Heart
- ❏ Horseshoe
- ❏ Pencil
- ❏ Razor
- ❏ Ring
- ❏ Top hat
- ❏ Worm

A DAY
AT
DINO-LAND

FIND THESE ITEMS...

- ❏ Bone
- ❏ Bow tie
- ❏ Fire hydrant
- ❏ Fish
- ❏ Flower
- ❏ Flower pot
- ❏ Football
- ❏ Heart
- ❏ Hot-air balloon
- ❏ Necktie
- ❏ Net
- ❏ Pencil
- ❏ Periscope
- ❏ Pick
- ❏ Pizza delivery dino
- ❏ Plunger
- ❏ Screwdriver
- ❏ Shark fin
- ❏ Shovel
- ❏ Skier
- ❏ Sled
- ❏ Sunglasses
- ❏ Suspenders
- ❏ Tire

MUSEUM-A-SAURUS

FIND THESE ITEMS...

- ❏ Arrow
- ❏ Astronaut
- ❏ Bib
- ❏ Broom
- ❏ Camera
- ❏ Cane
- ❏ Crack
- ❏ Crown
- ❏ Dart
- ❏ Eyeglasses
- ❏ Fish
- ❏ Flower
- ❏ Golf club
- ❏ Heart
- ❏ Hourglass
- ❏ Menu
- ❏ Moustache
- ❏ Nail
- ❏ Pencils (3)
- ❏ Pizza delivery dino
- ❏ Rock
- ❏ Roll
- ❏ Telescope
- ❏ Toothbrush
- ❏ Top hat
- ❏ Umbrella
- ❏ Volcano
- ❏ Yo-yo

FIND CUPID
AMONG THESE
CARTOON
FAVORITES

AND THESE FUN ITEMS:

- ❏ Balloons (4)
- ❏ Banana peel
- ❏ Baseball
- ❏ Basket
- ❏ Beehive
- ❏ Bone
- ❏ Cactus
- ❏ Candle
- ❏ Cup
- ❏ Feather
- ❏ Flowers (2)
- ❏ Flying bats (2)
- ❏ Hearts (10)
- ❏ Lock
- ❏ Magic lamp
- ❏ Mirror
- ❏ Mushroom
- ❏ Musical note
- ❏ Painted egg
- ❏ Piggy bank
- ❏ Pirate
- ❏ Pizzas (2)
- ❏ Tire
- ❏ Top hat
- ❏ Turtle
- ❏ Umbrella

FIND CUPID
IN
VERONA

AND THESE FUN ITEMS:

- ❏ Baseball cap
- ❏ Bird
- ❏ Bull's-eye
- ❏ Candy cane
- ❏ Duck
- ❏ Fishing pole
- ❏ Football player
- ❏ Frog
- ❏ Hamburger
- ❏ Hot dog
- ❏ Ice skates
- ❏ Key
- ❏ Kites (2)
- ❏ Light bulb
- ❏ Mouse
- ❏ Paper airplane
- ❏ Pie
- ❏ Pillow
- ❏ Propeller
- ❏ Roller skates
- ❏ Saw
- ❏ Skateboard
- ❏ Sock
- ❏ Stars (3)
- ❏ Sunglasses
- ❏ Television

FIND CUPID
AT
WASHINGTON'S WEDDING

AND THESE FUN ITEMS:

- ❏ Apple
- ❏ Banana peel
- ❏ Bone
- ❏ Bonnet
- ❏ Bowling ball
- ❏ Butterfly
- ❏ Camera
- ❏ Candy cane
- ❏ Chalkboard
- ❏ Crayon
- ❏ Drumstick
- ❏ Egg
- ❏ Feathers (4)
- ❏ Firecracker
- ❏ Fish (2)
- ❏ Hearts (4)
- ❏ Kites (2)
- ❏ Knight
- ❏ Mouse
- ❏ Pizza
- ❏ Rabbits (2)
- ❏ Shovel
- ❏ Snail
- ❏ Socks (3)
- ❏ Surfboard
- ❏ Toaster
- ❏ Umbrella
- ❏ Witch's hats (2)

FIND CUPID
IN
SHERWOOD FOREST

AND THESE FUN ITEMS:

- ☐ Balloon
- ☐ Bell
- ☐ Birdcage
- ☐ Broom
- ☐ Cactus
- ☐ Camel
- ☐ Candle
- ☐ Car
- ☐ Clock
- ☐ Eagle
- ☐ Elephant
- ☐ Feathers (3)
- ☐ Fish (2)
- ☐ Fishing pole
- ☐ Fork
- ☐ Ghosts (2)
- ☐ Gold coin
- ☐ Golf club
- ☐ Humpty Dumpty
- ☐ Igloo
- ☐ Ladder
- ☐ Mice (2)
- ☐ Owl
- ☐ Paintbrush
- ☐ Slingshot
- ☐ Star
- ☐ Sunglasses
- ☐ Turtles (3)

FIND CUPID
ON THIS
MOONLIT NIGHT

AND THESE FUN ITEMS:

- ❏ Arrows (2)
- ❏ Axe
- ❏ Bearded man
- ❏ Bell
- ❏ Bone
- ❏ Bowling ball
- ❏ Broken heart
- ❏ Broom
- ❏ Comb
- ❏ Cradle
- ❏ Dog
- ❏ Flying bat
- ❏ Frying pan
- ❏ Hot dog
- ❏ Lost boot
- ❏ Owl
- ❏ Pencil
- ❏ Pie
- ❏ Rabbit
- ❏ Santa Claus
- ❏ Scissors
- ❏ Skateboard
- ❏ Squirrel
- ❏ Telescope
- ❏ Unicorn

FIND CUPID
AMONG THE
FALLING
LEAVES

AND THESE FUN ITEMS:

- ❏ Ball of yarn
- ❏ Balloon
- ❏ Banana peel
- ❏ Bat under a hat
- ❏ Bottle
- ❏ Broken dish
- ❏ Butterfly
- ❏ Cat
- ❏ Crayon
- ❏ Drum
- ❏ Duck
- ❏ Fishing pole
- ❏ Football player
- ❏ Golf ball
- ❏ Goose
- ❏ Hammer
- ❏ Hoe
- ❏ Igloo
- ❏ Key
- ❏ Kite
- ❏ Knife
- ❏ Paper airplane
- ❏ Pigs (2)
- ❏ Pumpkin
- ❏ Rat in a cap
- ❏ Skateboard
- ❏ Umpire

FIND CUPID
IN THE
CROCKETT'S YARD

AND THESE FUN ITEMS:

- ☐ Apple
- ☐ Axe
- ☐ Ball
- ☐ Baskets (2)
- ☐ Bears (3)
- ☐ Beaver
- ☐ Bee
- ☐ Bone
- ☐ Broom
- ☐ Candle
- ☐ Chicken
- ☐ Child's wagon
- ☐ Cricket
- ☐ Dogs (2)
- ☐ Goldilocks
- ☐ Hearts (3)
- ☐ Lion
- ☐ Lost hat
- ☐ Moose
- ☐ Pinocchio
- ☐ Rain barrel
- ☐ Rake
- ☐ Shovel
- ☐ Snake
- ☐ Squirrel
- ☐ Tugboat
- ☐ Turkey
- ☐ Wagon wheel